AF594629

Jolly Phonics

Handwriting Book 1

s a t i p n

in print letters

Guidelines

Good pencil control and correct formation enable students to achieve neat, fluent and, eventually, joined handwriting.

Handwriting practice works best when the students are sitting at their table or desk. This provides a firm flat surface to write on and encourages correct posture.

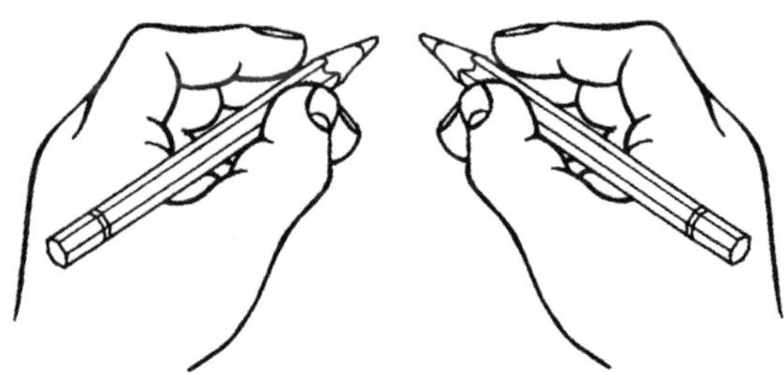

A good pencil hold from the very beginning is extremely important for developing neat, fluent handwriting. The tripod pencil grip is recommended.

Hold the pencil between the thumb and index finger, and support it on the middle finger. As the pencil is moved, the knuckles on the thumb and index finger look like a frog's legs.

Coloring is also a good way to develop fine motor skills. Encourage the students to color carefully, to keep within the lines, and to choose appropriate colors.

Spot the frog

Encourage the students to look out for the frog throughout these books, to remind them to practice their "froggy-leg" grip.

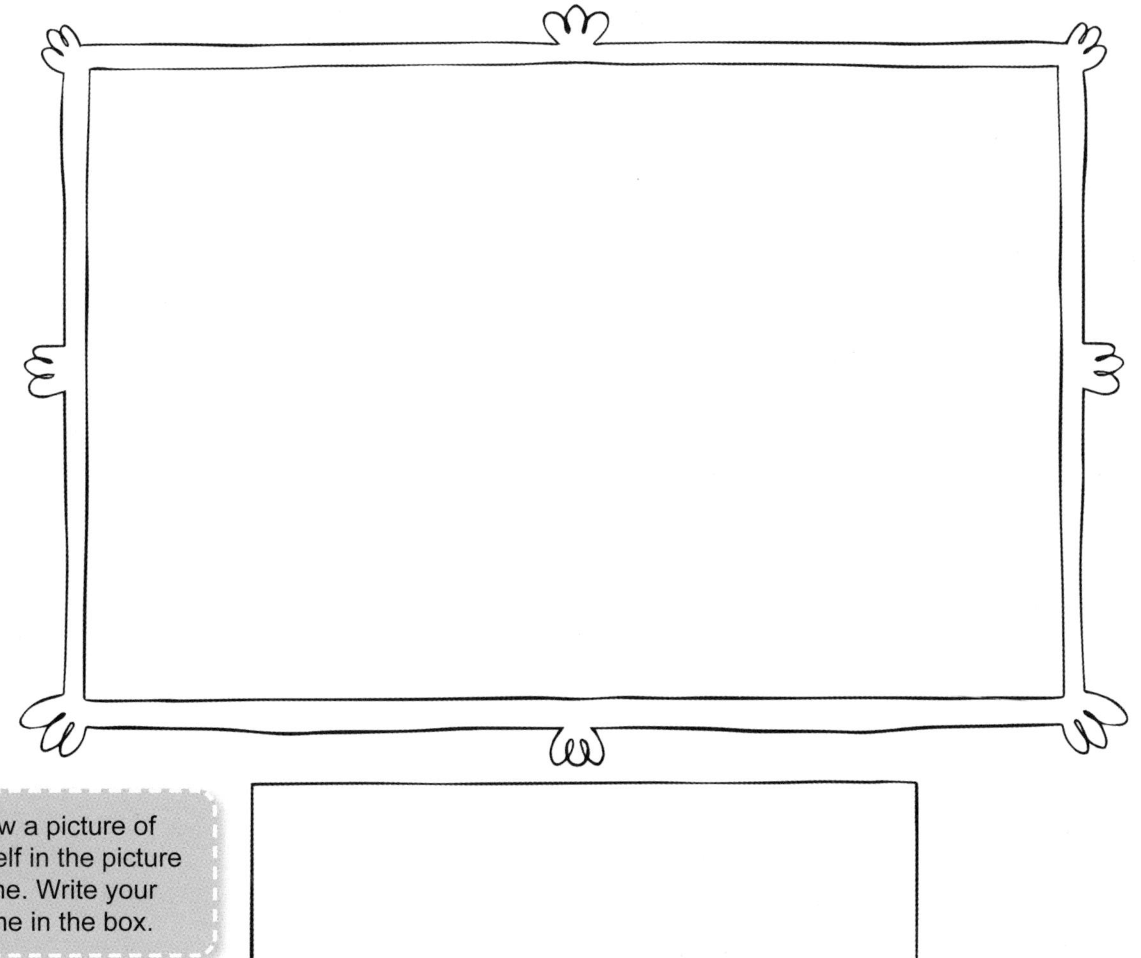

Draw a picture of yourself in the picture frame. Write your name in the box.

Trace the animal trails.

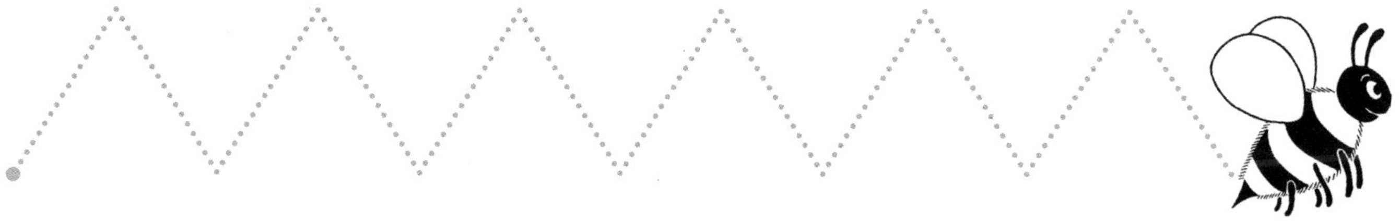

Finish each animal's trail.

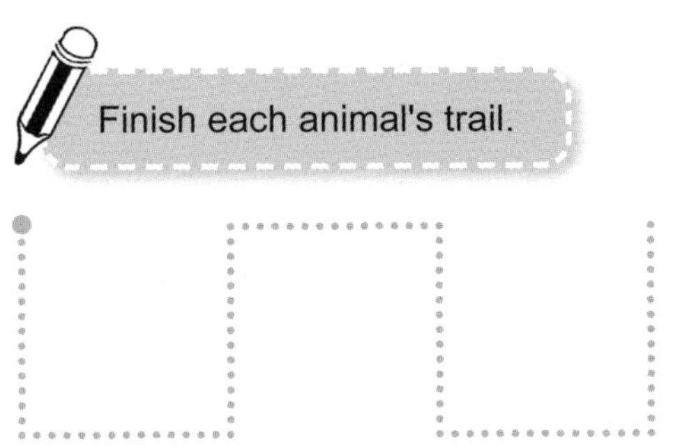

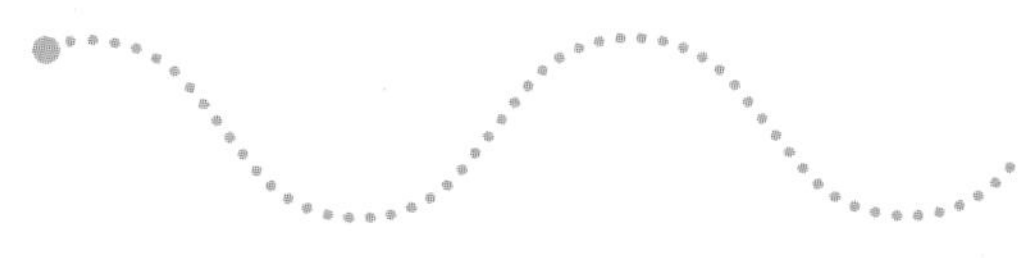

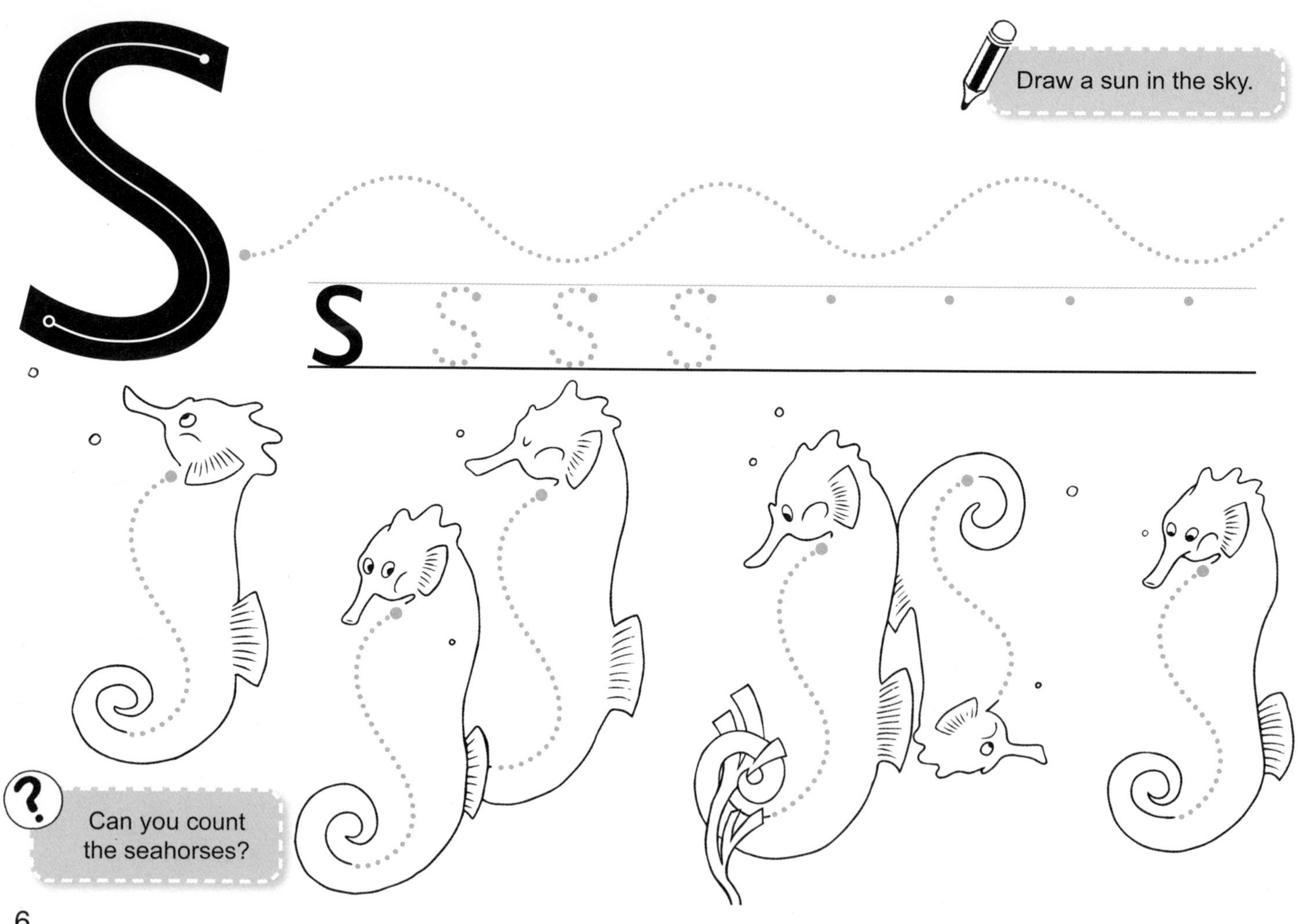
S
Draw a sun in the sky.
s
Can you count the seahorses?

s s

What animals can you see in the seaweed?

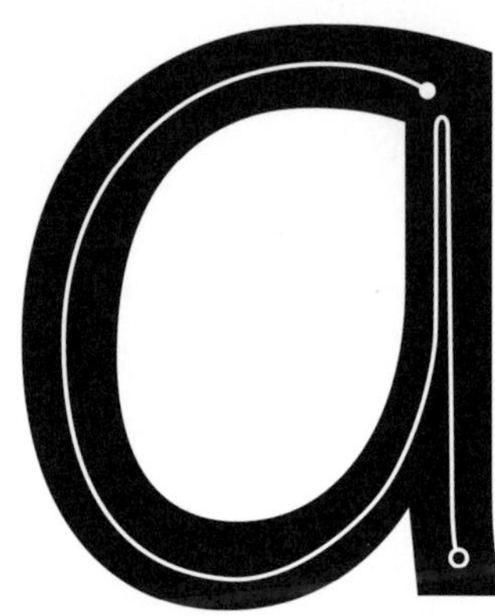

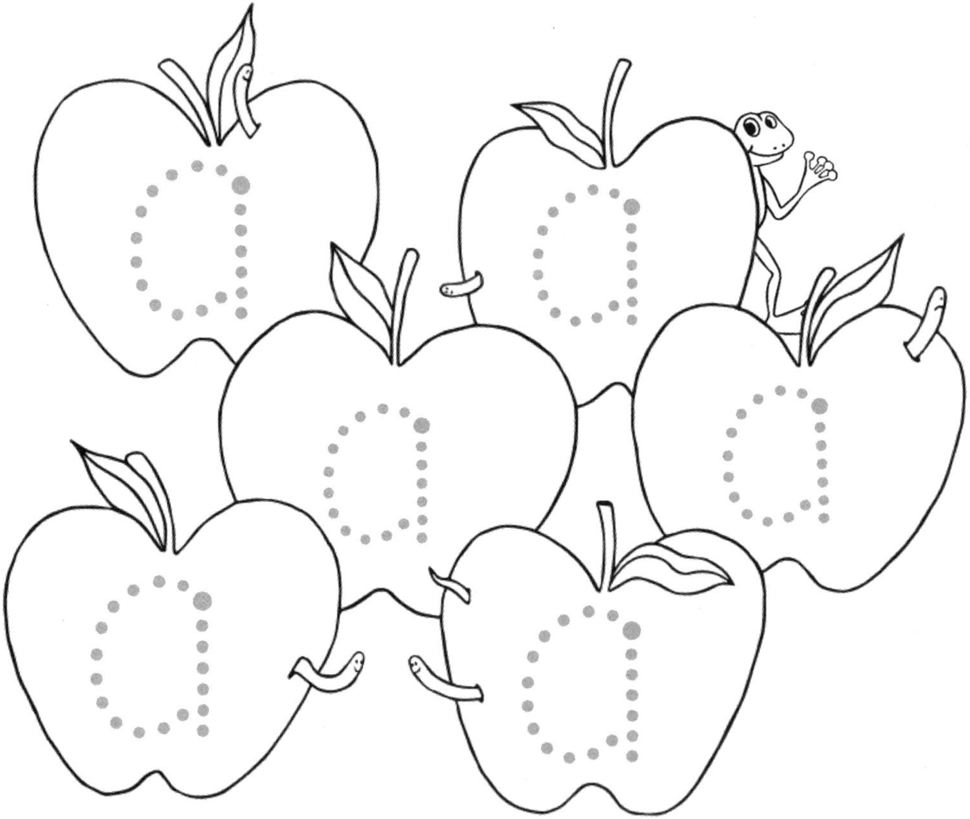

Help the ant find an apple without a worm in it.

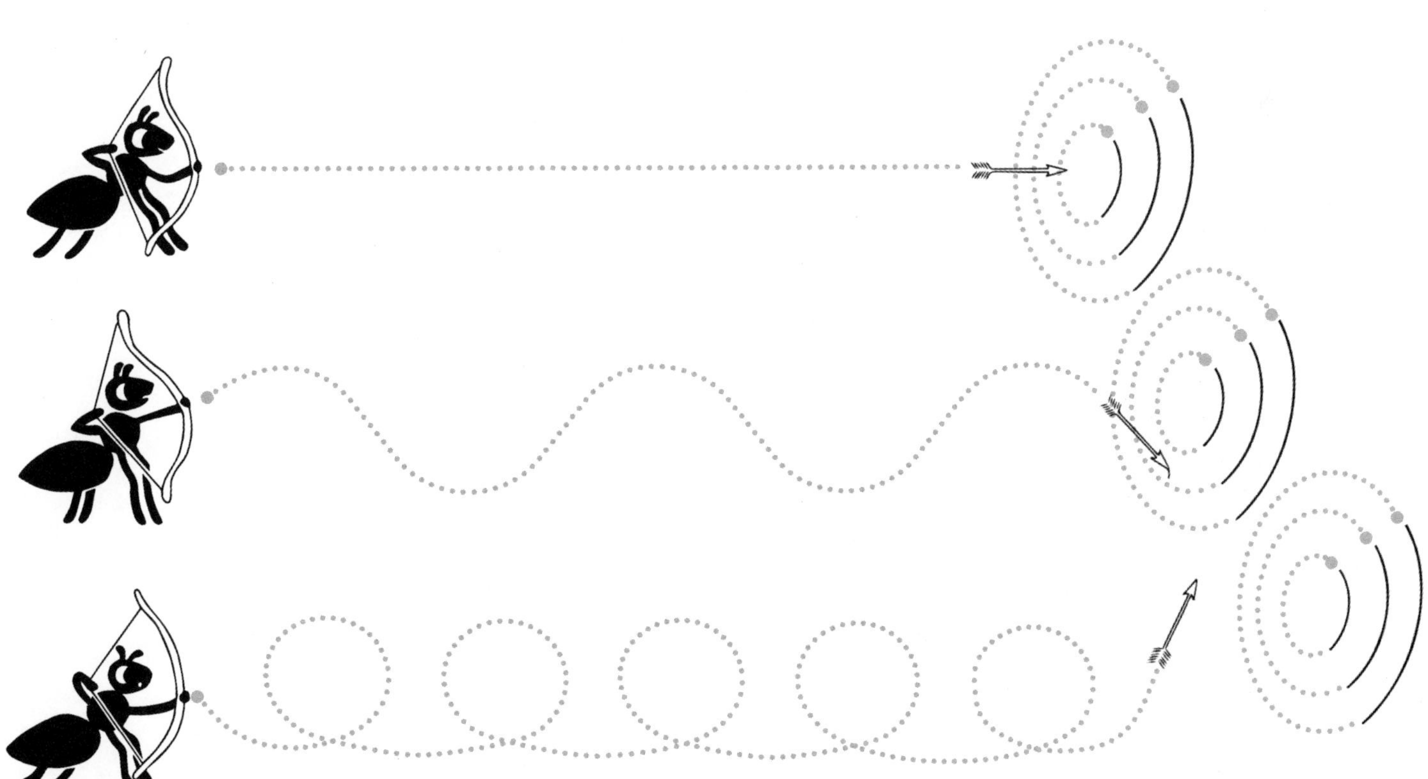

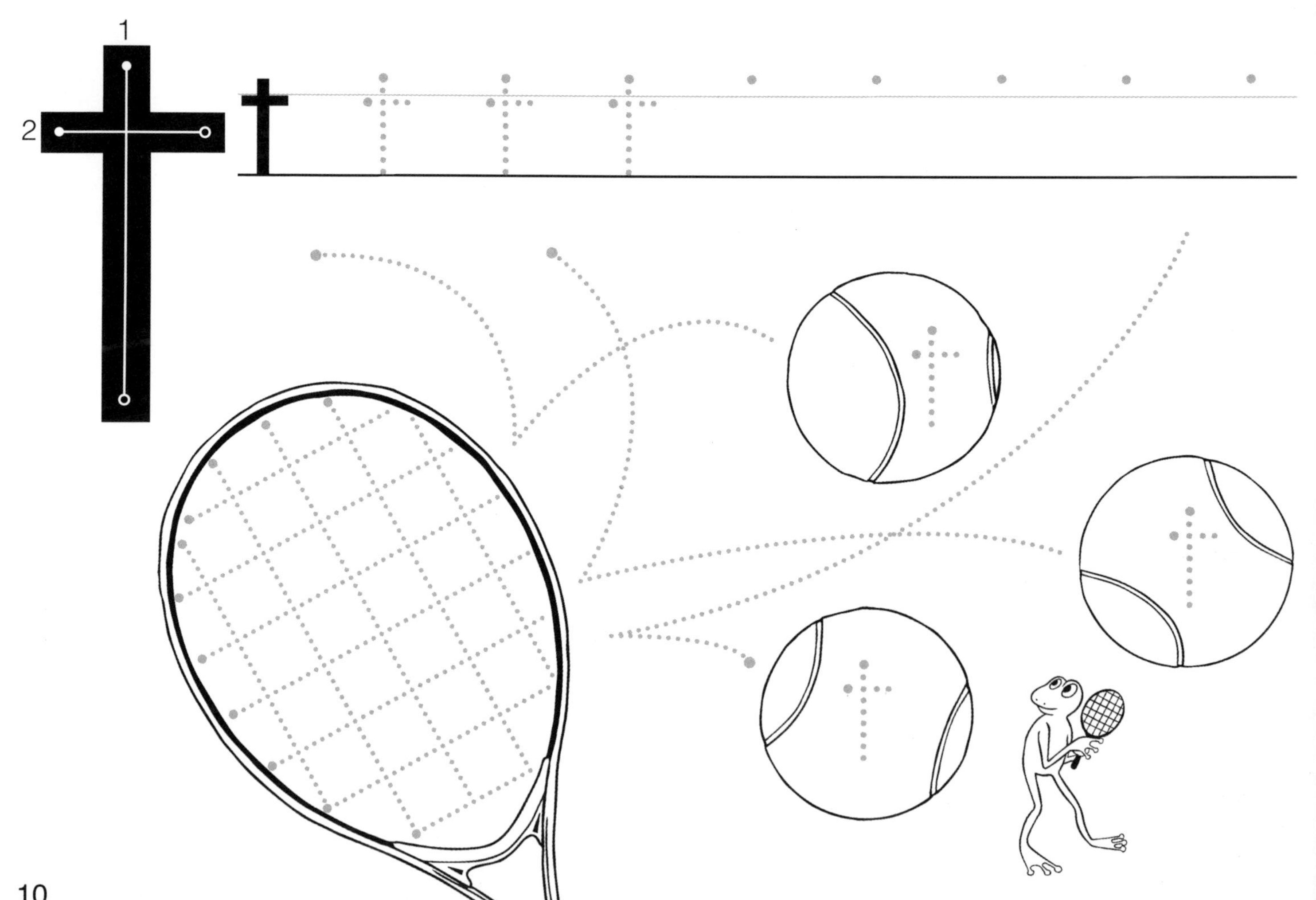
1
2
t

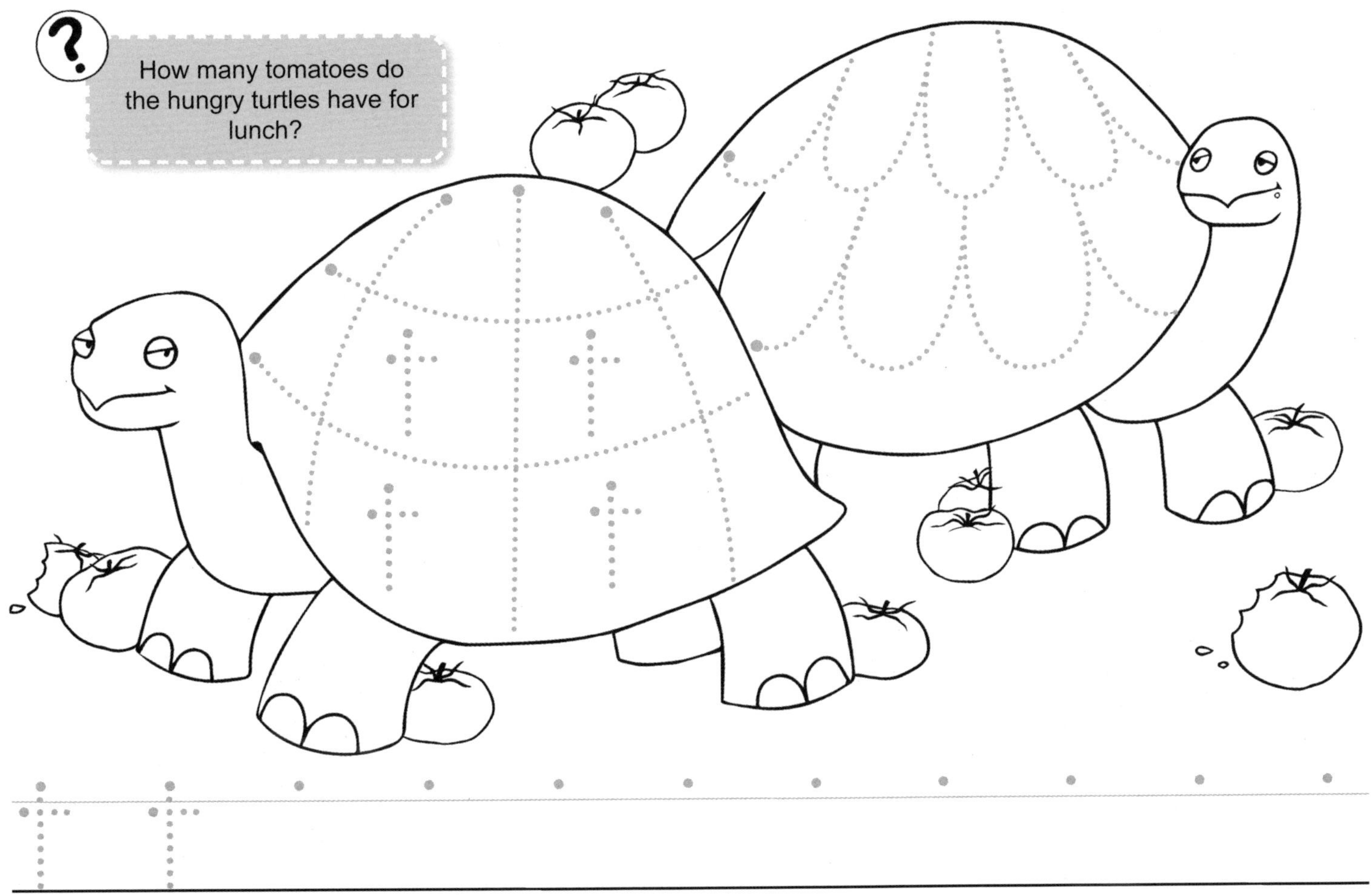
How many tomatoes do the hungry turtles have for lunch?

Help the ant find its way home.

Trace the lines.

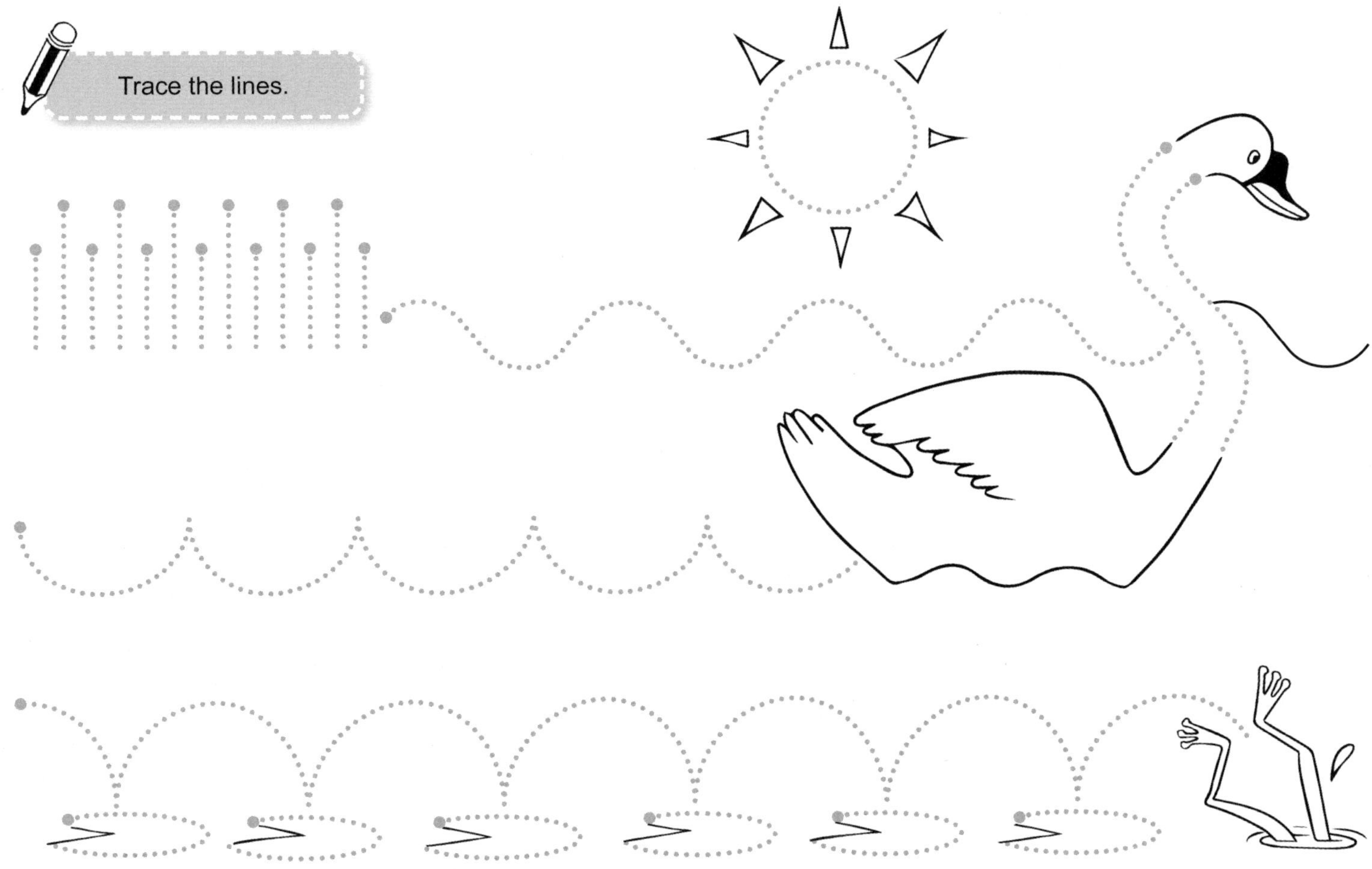

2
1
i
sit

s s a a

Color the parrots pink and purple.

p

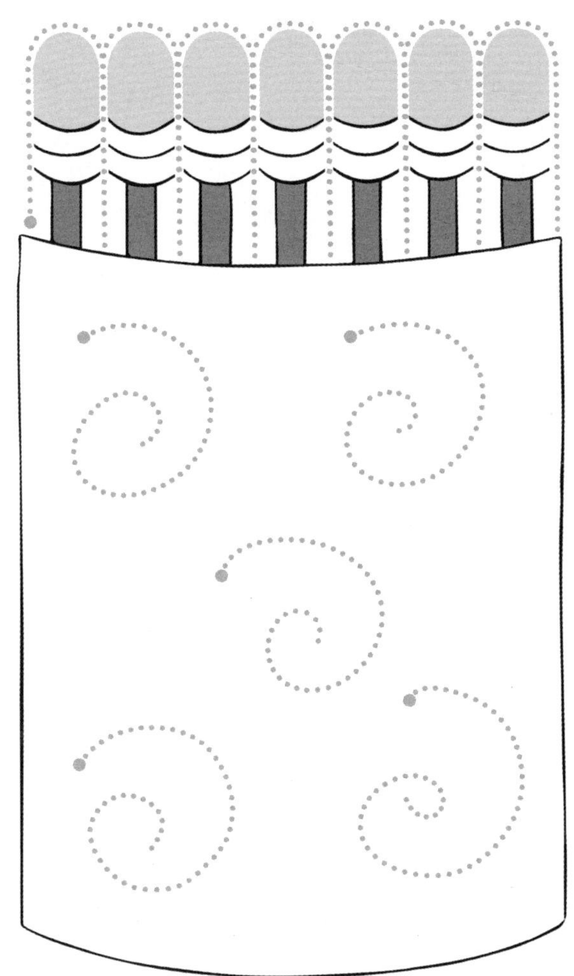

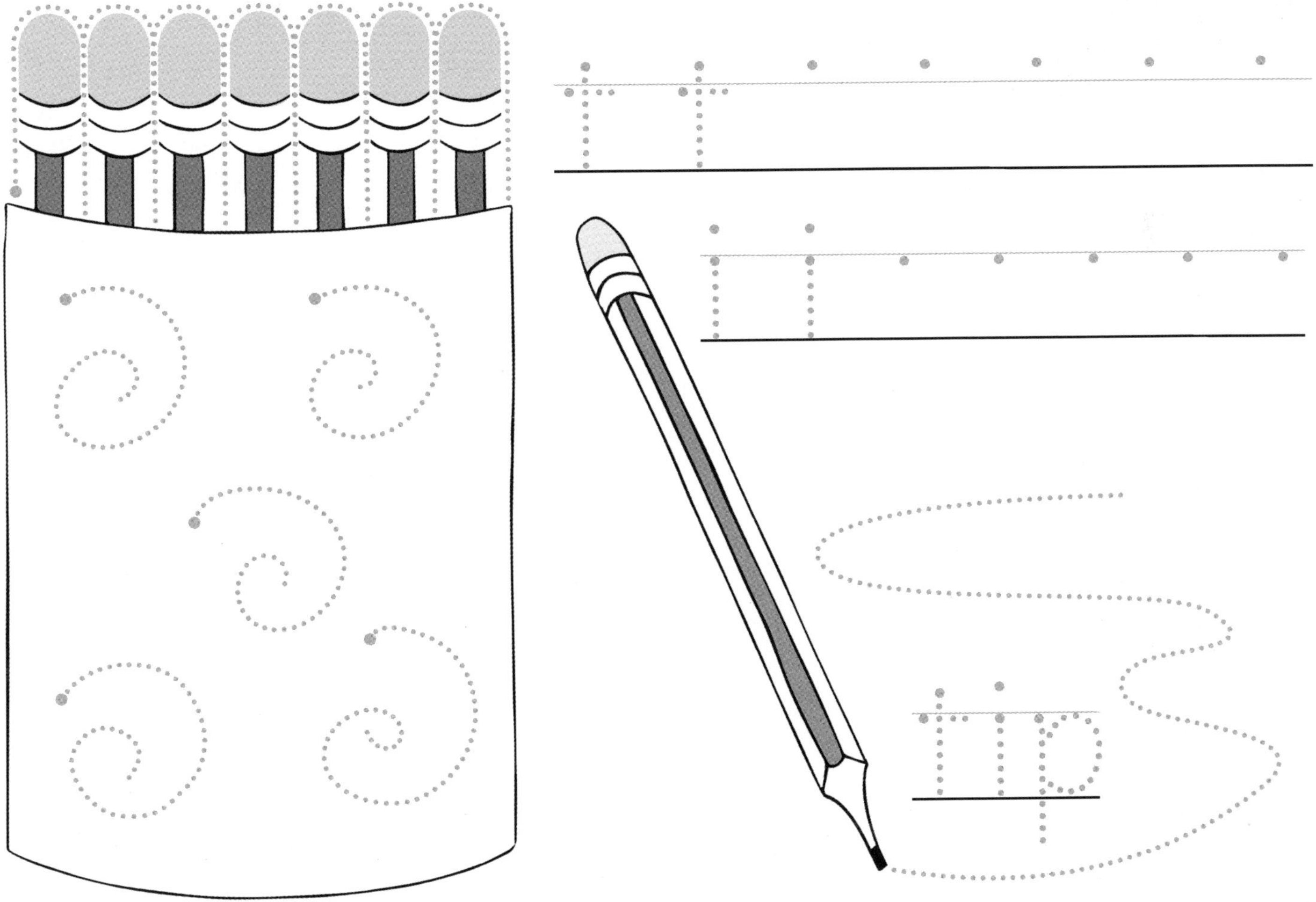

rr

rr

rrp

n
What's cooking in the pan? Can you think of any more foods with an /n/ sound in?
pan
n n n n

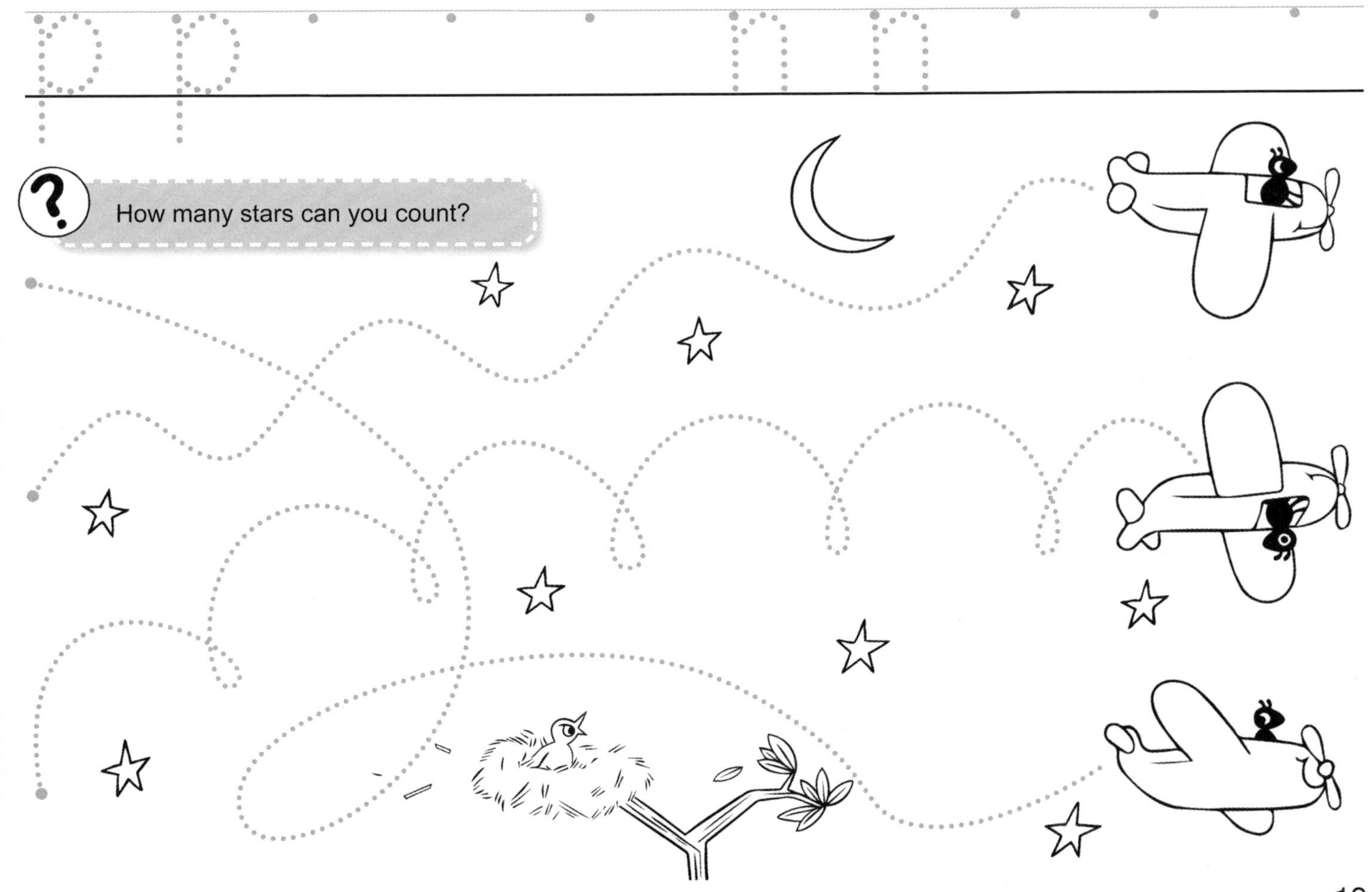
How many stars can you count?

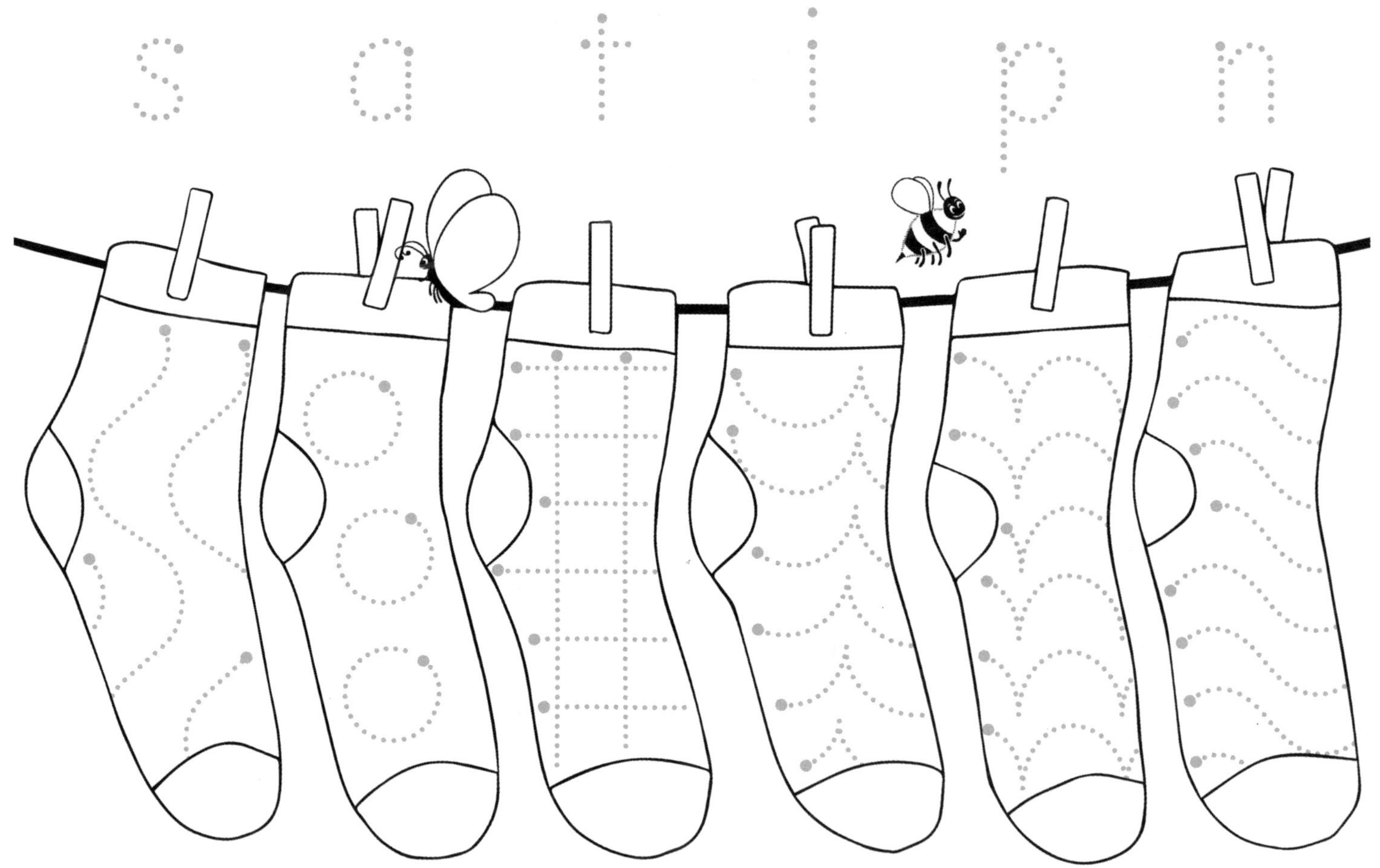
s a t i p n

ants in pants

Can you draw something that begins with each sound?

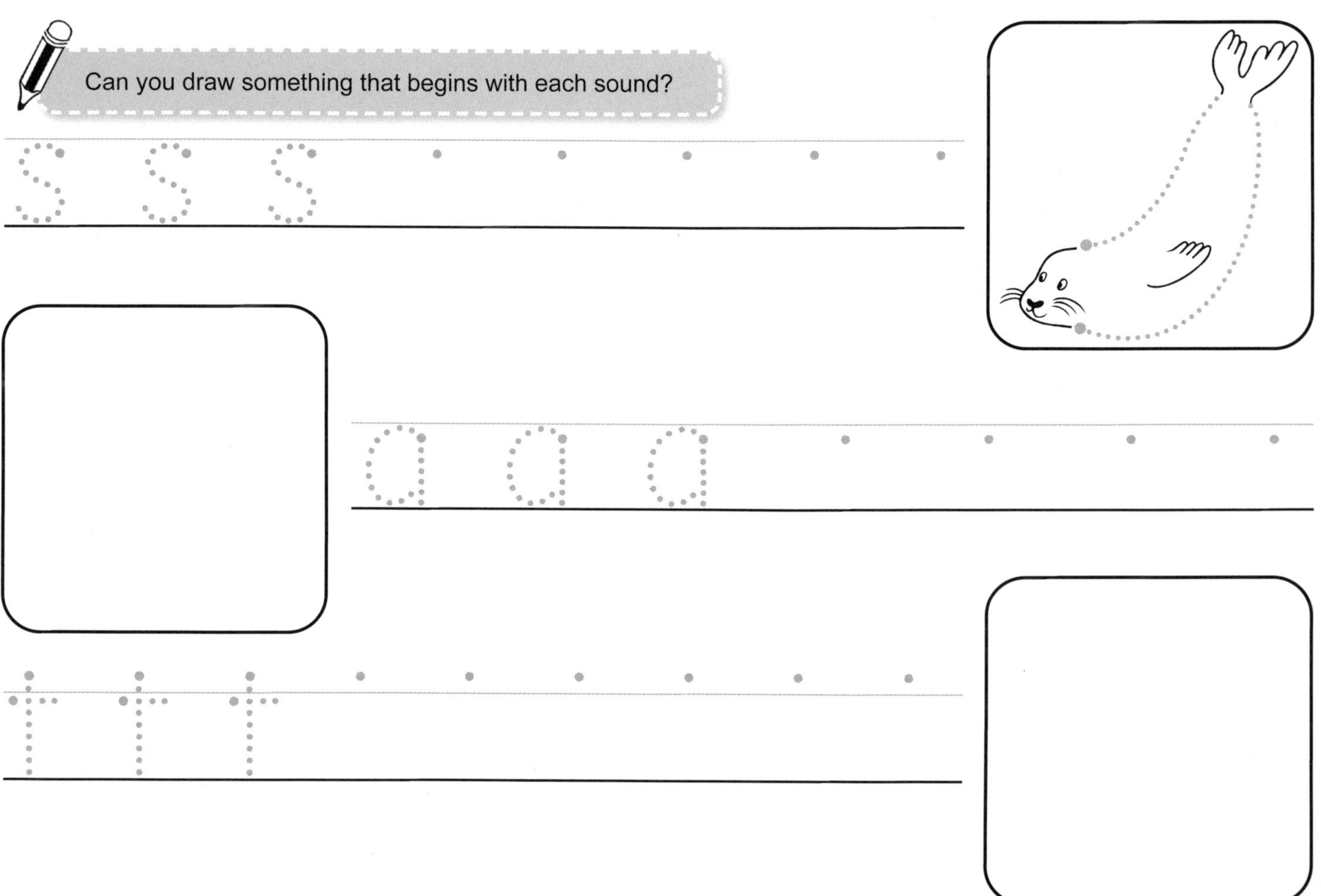

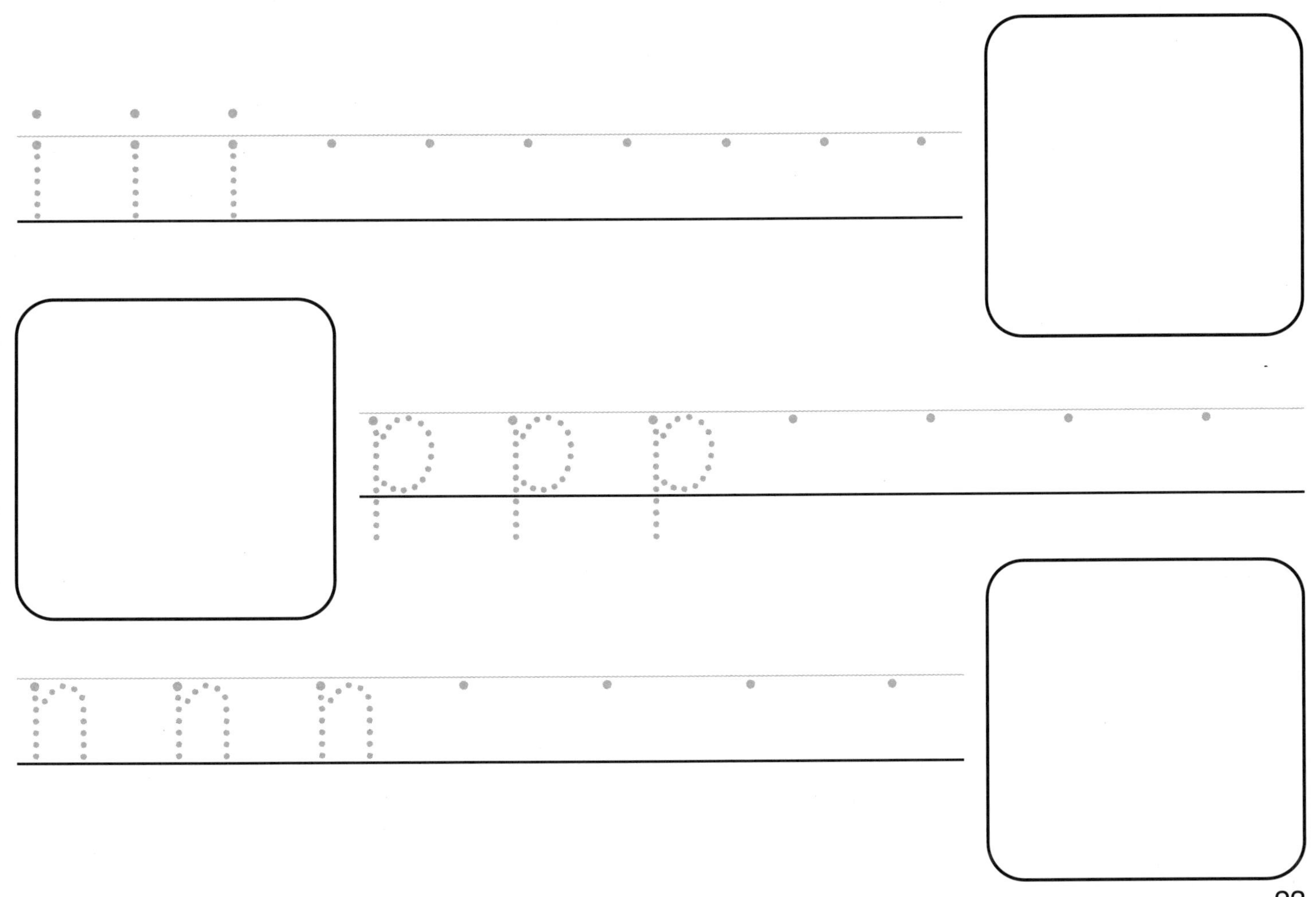

Ages 4+

Jolly Phonics Handwriting Book

Perfect for practicing letter formation

These handwriting books provide letter formation practice for beginner writers. Dotted letters and words (with starting dots) remind students how the letters are formed, and encourage them to write words using the letter sounds they know.
Each page features fun activities to complete and attractive pictures to color, which help the students to develop fine motor control.

This book contains the following letter sounds:

Group 1:	s a t i p n
Group 2:	c k e h r m d
Group 3:	g o u l f b
Group 4:	ai j oa ie ee or
Group 5:	z w ng v oo oo
Group 6:	y x ch sh th th
Group 7:	qu ou oi ue er ar

To see the full range of Jolly Phonics products, visit our website at www.jollylearning.com

MIX
Paper | Supporting responsible forestry
FSC® C016973

ISBN 978-1-83582-181-7

Reference: JL1817

82 Winter Sport Lane, Williston, VT 05495, USA. Tel: +1-800-488-2665
77 Hornbeam Road, Buckhurst Hill, Essex, IG9 6JX, UK. Tel: +44 20 8501 0405
Printed in China.

www.jollylearning.com info@jollylearning.co.uk